# LET'S PRETEND

## CLARE BEATON

Published by Barron's Educational Series, Inc.
250 Wireless Boulevard, Hauppauge, NY 11788
© b small publishing 1997
Written by Clare Beaton
ISBN: 0-7641-0116-1
Library of Congress Catalog Card Number 97-70385
Printed in Hong Kong
987654321

# CONTENTS

## TO PARENTS AND TEACHERS

- Children love to role-play, and while they are having fun, they are also learning. Among other skills, they are practicing:
  - ★ cooperating and socializing
  - ★ discussing and negotiating
  - ★ drawing and coloring
  - ★ reading and writing
  - ★ counting and money
  - ★ cutting out and constructing
  - ★ cooking.

- The ideas in this book are not meant to replace the children's own imaginative play but are to give them extra ideas. They may want to select just one or two, or these might spark off new ideas of their own.

- Be sensitive about joining in the pretend play. You might be able to provide equipment or materials and you should supervise cooking or using a craft knife or sharp tools. If you play a role yourself, take the lead from the children: enter fully into the make-believe but don't dominate. Teachers can carefully steer the game to cover a particular learning area.

- Try to keep collections of cardboard boxes, dress-up clothes, old make-up, old packaging, greetings cards, gift wrap, and so on that the children can raid.

- Store props they have made to play with over again. Put them in separate boxes and label clearly.

- The activities in this book can give you ideas for other role-play topics. Here are some suggestions:
  - ★ a sports day or Olympic Games
  - ★ an explorer expedition
  - ★ a circus
  - ★ a cabaret
  - ★ an art and craft show
  - ★ going back or forward in time: castles, pirates, spaceships, time machines
  - ★ other well-known fairy tales.

## BE SAFE!

- ★ Make sure the children take great care when using sharp equipment: scissors, craft knife, pins and needles, and so on.
- ★ Make sure an adult supervises any cooking using a hot stove or an oven.
- ★ Check and follow manufacturer's instructions for face paints, hair gels and sprays, fabric paints, and so on. Test for allergies if necessary.

# LET'S PLAY RESTAURANT

# CHARACTERS

A restaurant needs a cook, waiters, waitresses, and of course some customers. Take turns playing all these parts. Invite your friends to join in.

**waitress**

Wear black and white.

apron

**cook**

large white hankie

**waiter**

Dress up.

**customers**

# WHAT TO WEAR

Look at the pictures on page 4. You can make these simple costumes.

## bow tie

15.6 inches ribbon or elastic

staple

staple

Cut from thick black cardboard.

Put the bow tie around your neck under your collar.

large white hankie

safety pins

Tie on pencil to write down the orders.

Use stickers.

**ANN** **TOM** **JOE**

## name tags for waiters

## aprons
Use one you have at home, or make your own with a hankie fastened on with safety pins.

## Make a chef's hat

You will need:
• thin white cardboard
• adhesive tape and scissors
• ruler and pencil
• white crêpe paper

## hats and handbags for the customers

white crêpe paper

15.6 in.

same length as cardboard

Tape to cardboard.

Tape together.

2¾ in.

Cut a strip of cardboard 2¾ inches wide, and long enough to go around your head, plus 1 inch.

Cut paper. Gather one side. Tape it together to make the top of the hat.

Tape the other side to the cardboard strip and tape the ends together.

# HOW TO SET UP YOUR RESTAURANT

You need tables, chairs, food, and drinks. Decorate your restaurant so more customers will want to come in. In the summer you could set up tables and chairs outside.

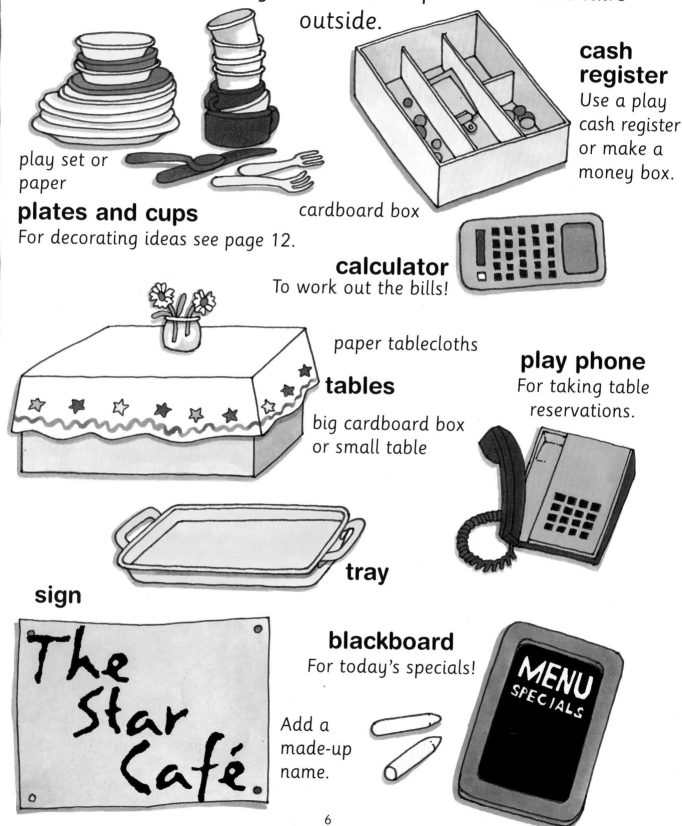

**cash register**
Use a play cash register or make a money box.

play set or paper
**plates and cups**
For decorating ideas see page 12.

cardboard box

**calculator**
To work out the bills!

paper tablecloths

**tables**
big cardboard box or small table

**play phone**
For taking table reservations.

**tray**

**sign**

The Star Café.

**blackboard**
For today's specials!

Add a made-up name.

MENU SPECIALS

# FOOD

There are lots of ways of making food for your restaurant. You could serve real food like muffins, raisins, and slices of vegetables and fruit. Or you could make play food. Remember, only cook with an adult!

## play food

You could cut food pictures out of magazines or draw pictures of different foods and stick them onto paper plates.

Make pizzas by cutting out big circles of thick cardboard.

Then add red felt-tip tomato sauce.

Add small pink circles of pepperoni, or ham, cut from colored paper.

Finally add yellow tissue paper cheese.

7

# Make playdough ice cream

You will need:
- old saucepan and wooden spoon
- 14 oz. flour
- 7 oz. salt
- $3\frac{1}{2}$ tablespoons cream of tartar
- $\frac{1}{2}$ tablespoon cooking oil
- $3\frac{1}{4}$ c. water
- food colorings or powder paints
- colored paper to decorate.

★ Ask an adult to help! Put everything (except the paper and food colorings or powder paints) in a saucepan and heat. Boil until it is thick, stirring all the time.

Leave it to cool, then knead the dough mixture. Divide the dough into 3 big lumps. Add a different color to each one to make 3 "flavors."

Use a spoon to dish out scoops to make ice cream sundaes. Cut out small pieces of colored paper to make sprinkles to decorate them.

# Make a playdough hamburger

You will need:
- playdough recipe (as above)
- food colorings

Divide the playdough in half. Make the bun out of one half.

Divide remaining dough into small balls for hamburger, lettuce, tomato, and cheese.

Color each ball, roll out, and cut into shapes.

Put hamburger together and serve on a paper plate.

Prick top with fork.

# DRINKS

If you don't want to make food, you could just serve drinks in your restaurant. Make a list of the drinks you can make to show your customers their choices.

### milkshake
Fresh fruit, ice cream, and milk mixed together in a blender

### fruit punch
Fruit juice mixed with ice and pieces of fruit

umbrellas

### fruit fizz
Fruit juice mixed with carbonated water or lemonade. Add ice cubes colored with food coloring.

### ice cream float
Lemonade or cola with a scoop of ice cream

# MENUS AND TABLE CARDS

Plan your menu first. You could make a list of just the types of pizza and the flavors of ice cream you have made. Or you could have a menu with appetizers, main courses, desserts, and drinks.

## menu

Decorate it with pictures or drawings of food.

Write your menu on a piece of folded paper.

Put a price beside each item.

## table cards

Fold a small rectangle of thick paper in half and write a table number on each one.

If you have a small bell you could make a "ring for service" card too.

Decorate your cards.

# PAPERWORK!

There is lots of paperwork to do if you run a restaurant!

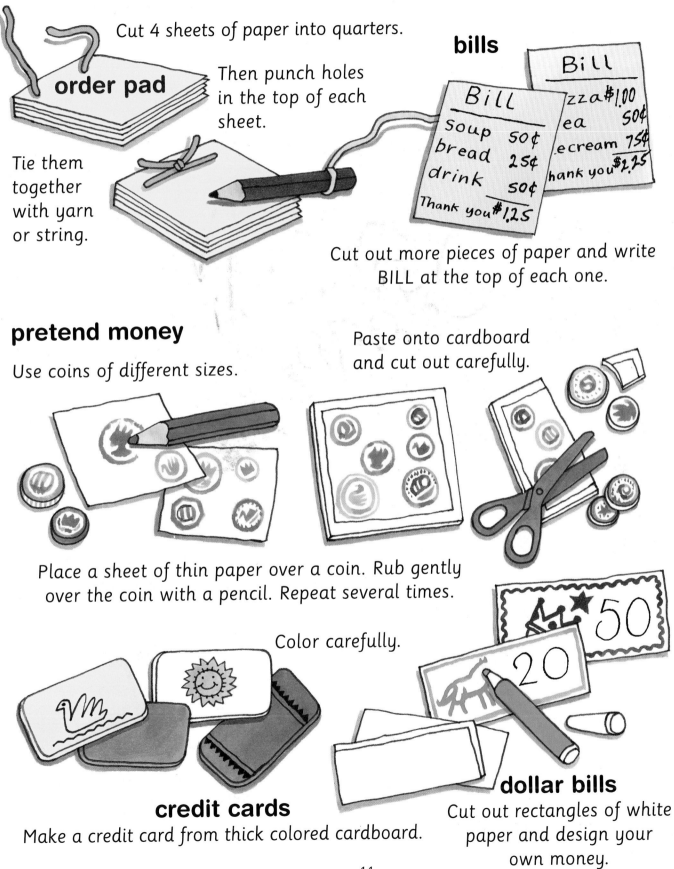

Cut 4 sheets of paper into quarters.

**order pad**

Then punch holes in the top of each sheet.

Tie them together with yarn or string.

**bills**

Bill
soup 50¢
bread 25¢
drink 50¢
Thank you $1.25

Bill
zza $1.00
ea 50¢
ecream 75¢
hank you $1.25

Cut out more pieces of paper and write BILL at the top of each one.

**pretend money**

Use coins of different sizes.

Paste onto cardboard and cut out carefully.

Place a sheet of thin paper over a coin. Rub gently over the coin with a pencil. Repeat several times.

Color carefully.

**credit cards**

Make a credit card from thick colored cardboard.

**dollar bills**

Cut out rectangles of white paper and design your own money.

# DECORATE YOUR RESTAURANT

Think of a name for your restaurant. Call it something simple like The Star Café. Then you could decorate all your tablecloths, napkins, plates, cups, table cards, and menus with stars.

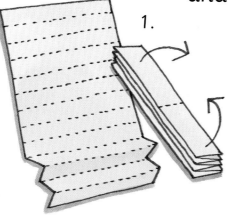

## folding napkins

1 Open up a paper napkin and fold it in half. Pleat it by folding evenly.
2 Fold the pleated napkin in two.
3 Put the folded end into a glass and pull the pleats out into a fan.

## decorating napkins

Fold the napkin to make a triangle.

Write the name of your restaurant or draw a picture. Loop the corners around and tuck one corner inside the other.

## tablecloths

Decorate your tablecloth with felt-tip pens or stickers to match your napkins.

## plates and cups

Decorate paper plates and cups with the pattern you have chosen for your restaurant.

# LET'S PLAY HOSPITAL

# CHARACTERS

A hospital needs nurses, doctors, patients, and their visitors. Take turns being a doctor or patient and include your dolls and teddy bears.

big white shirt as jacket

white sneakers or other sensible shoes

**doctor**

**nurse**

**patients**

T-shirts

sweatsuit pants

**ambulance people**

**visitors**

# WHAT TO WEAR

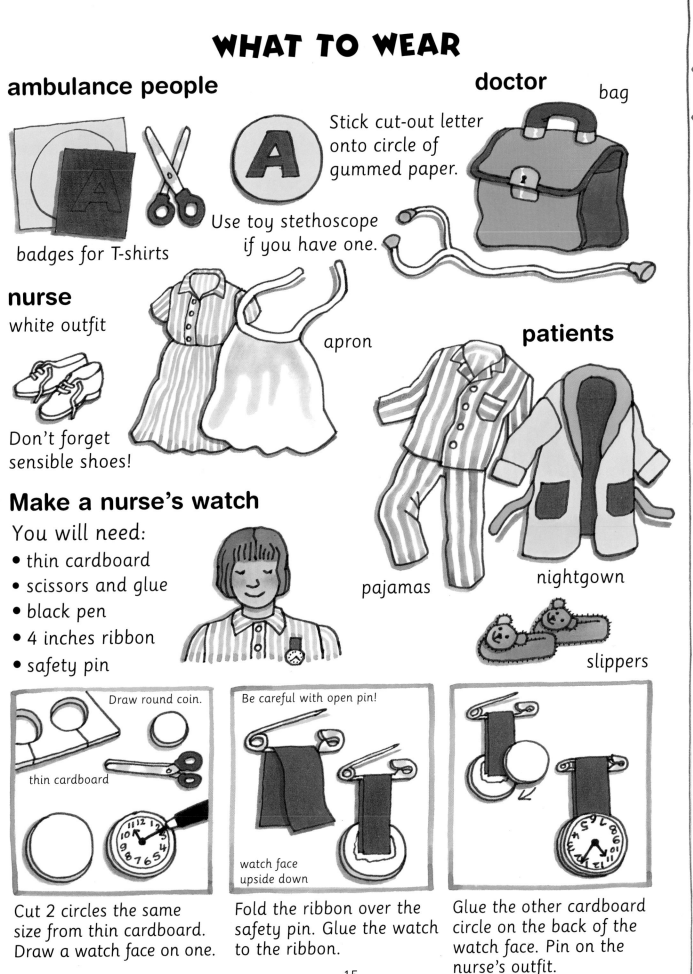

## ambulance people

badges for T-shirts

Stick cut-out letter onto circle of gummed paper.

Use toy stethoscope if you have one.

## doctor

bag

## nurse

white outfit

Don't forget sensible shoes!

apron

## patients

pajamas

nightgown

slippers

## Make a nurse's watch

You will need:
• thin cardboard
• scissors and glue
• black pen
• 4 inches ribbon
• safety pin

Draw round coin.

thin cardboard

Be careful with open pin!

watch face upside down

Cut 2 circles the same size from thin cardboard. Draw a watch face on one.

Fold the ribbon over the safety pin. Glue the watch to the ribbon.

Glue the other cardboard circle on the back of the watch face. Pin on the nurse's outfit.

# HOW TO SET UP YOUR HOSPITAL

You can use a real bed or a sofa, or push 2 chairs together for a bed. You can also use cushions on the floor.

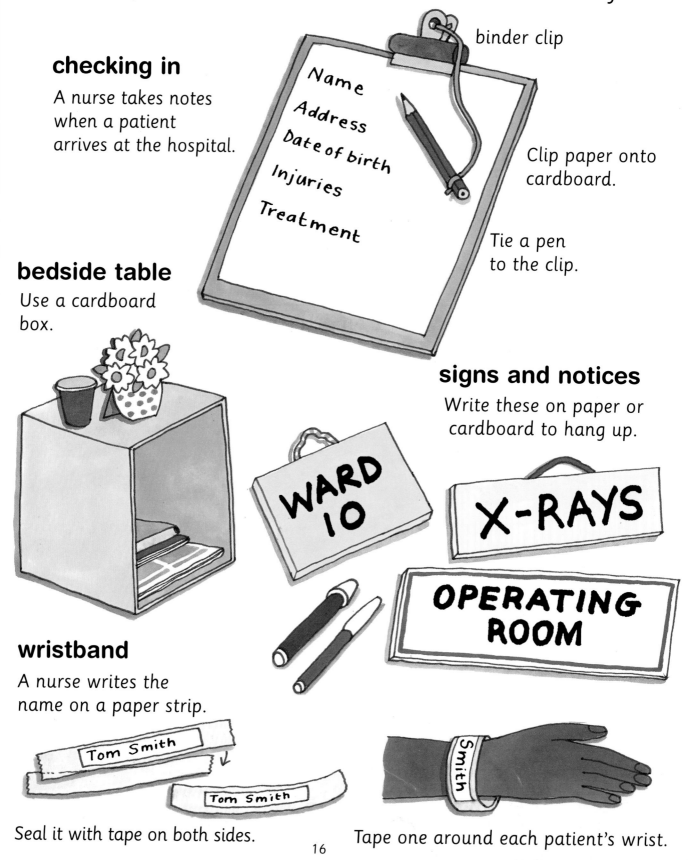

## checking in

A nurse takes notes when a patient arrives at the hospital.

binder clip

Name
Address
Date of birth
Injuries
Treatment

Clip paper onto cardboard.

Tie a pen to the clip.

## bedside table

Use a cardboard box.

## signs and notices

Write these on paper or cardboard to hang up.

WARD 10

X-RAYS

OPERATING ROOM

## wristband

A nurse writes the name on a paper strip.

Tom Smith

Tom Smith

Smith

Seal it with tape on both sides.

Tape one around each patient's wrist.

16

# INJURIES OR ILLNESS

## blood

Make with washable red paint and water, or tomato ketchup.
Keep away from eyes or mouth.

## stitches

Now bandage it up.

Clean up the blood with cotton balls or pads and cold water.

Then draw stitches with a black washable pen or face paints.

## bruises

Smudge dryish gray paint. Add yellow later.

## spots

Draw on with a red washable pen.

Use face paints to make the patients look ill!

## fever

Keep the patient cool (no bedclothes).
Give them lots of cold drinks.
Put a cold compress on their forehead (see page 19).

# ACCIDENTS

Sometimes people go to the hospital in an ambulance. The ambulance people make sure they are quiet and still on the journey.

## ambulance

Use a chair for the driver's seat.
Cut a steering wheel from cardboard.

eeeeorrrrrr
eeeeorrrrrr

Lie the patient flat on 2 chairs or cushions.

Don't forget a bell or siren!

## emergency room

Doctors and nurses wear masks and caps.

folded handkerchief

## x-rays

Draw them in white chalk or use white paint on a black sheet of paper. Pin up on the window to look at.

## toy beds

Make these from shoe boxes.

## toy stretchers

Use a cloth taped around sticks.

# TREATMENT

Different illnesses and injuries need different treatments to make you better. Here are some ideas.

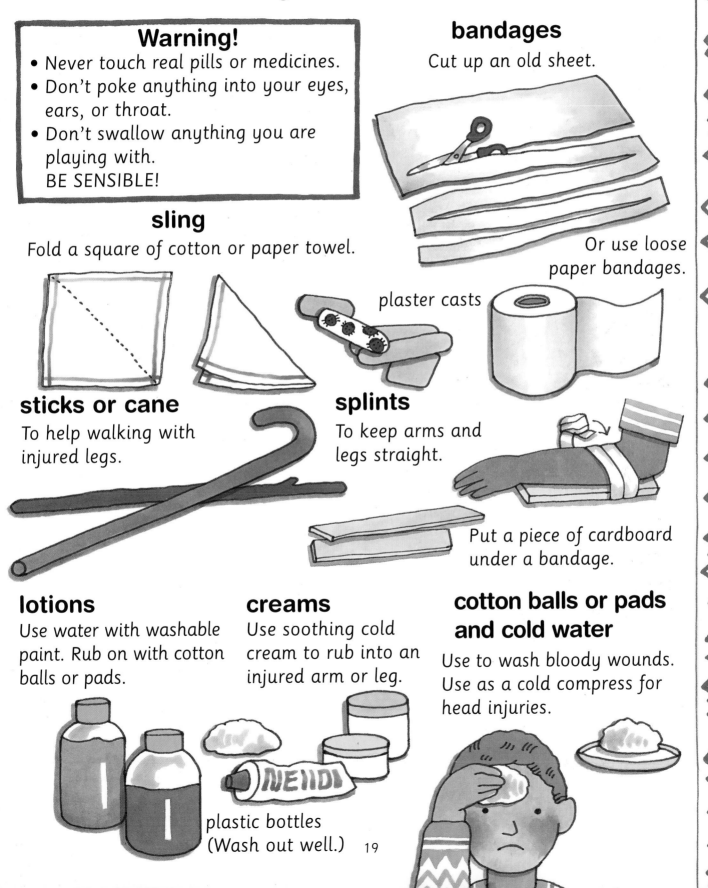

## Warning!
- Never touch real pills or medicines.
- Don't poke anything into your eyes, ears, or throat.
- Don't swallow anything you are playing with.
BE SENSIBLE!

## bandages
Cut up an old sheet.

Or use loose paper bandages.

## sling
Fold a square of cotton or paper towel.

plaster casts

## sticks or cane
To help walking with injured legs.

## splints
To keep arms and legs straight.

Put a piece of cardboard under a bandage.

## lotions
Use water with washable paint. Rub on with cotton balls or pads.

## creams
Use soothing cold cream to rub into an injured arm or leg.

## cotton balls or pads and cold water
Use to wash bloody wounds. Use as a cold compress for head injuries.

plastic bottles
(Wash out well.) 19

# GET BETTER SOON!

If you are ill, it is always nice to receive a get well card, especially when it is made just for you. Here are some things for the visitors to bring the patients.

### card

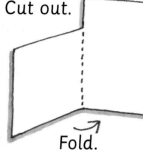

Cut out.

Fold.

Draw bed covers on the flap.

Draw a figure with the head above the flap.

Open up the bed flap and your ill friend or teddy bear is up and better!

## Make a vase of flowers

You will need:
- thick paper or thin cardboard
- scissors or craft knife
- colored pens

**fruit and drinks**

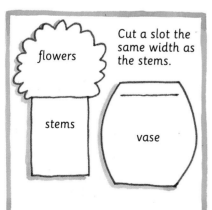

flowers

stems

vase

Cut a slot the same width as the stems.

Cut out a bunch of flowers with long stems. Cut out a vase a little taller than the stems.

Draw and color the flowers and vase.

Write a message on the back.

Push the flower stems through the slit in the vase. Stand it up.

20

# LET'S PLAY
# SCHOOL

# CHARACTERS

Take turns being the teacher and the students. You can have music and art teachers too.

**teachers**

**students**

**student's bag**

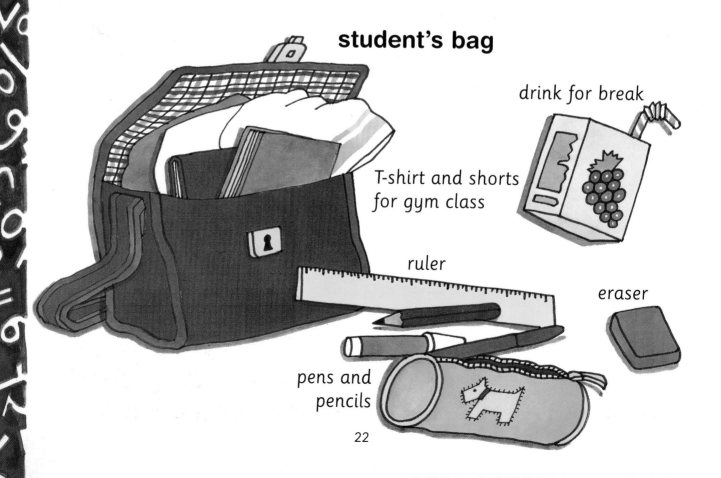

drink for break

T-shirt and shorts for gym class

ruler

eraser

pens and pencils

# EQUIPMENT

You will need desks or tables, chairs for the students, a blackboard, and posters or maps on the walls.

## posters and maps

Make these or use ready-made ones. Pin or stick on the wall. Get an adult's permission first!

Change the posters when you are learning about a special topic, like space or transportation.

Cut pictures from magazines.

## brushes, pens, and pencils

Cut up cardboard tubes and cover.

Label each one.

## globe

## bell

The teacher rings this for the start of school and break.

## books
reading and picture books

## paper
Recycle if possible.

**blackboard and chalk**

23

# THE SCHOOL DAY

## attendance

This is to check that everyone is at school! Write a list of the students' names.

The teacher calls attendance at the start of the day and checks off each name.

## LESSONS

## writing

• copy lines of letters.
• write a spelling list.
• write a short story.

## arithmetic

The teacher writes problems on the blackboard. The students copy them and work them out in their exercise books.

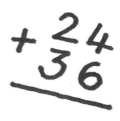

Use beans for adding and subtracting.

## reading

Take turns to read pages of a book out loud.

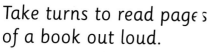

## music and singing

## computers

If you have one, use it for writing or drawing.

## nature study

Use a magnifying glass.

## painting

Hang paintings to dry.

## model making

Use playdough or modeling clay.

## alphabet or number display

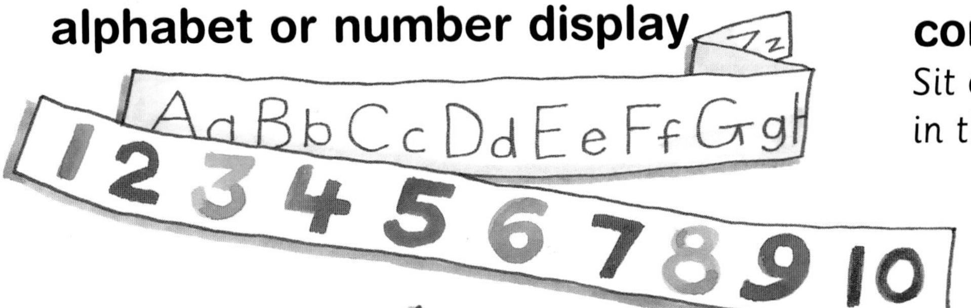

AaBbCcDdEeFfGg

1 2 3 4 5 6 7 8 9 10

## "time-out" corner

Sit on a chair in the corner.

Change into T-shirt and shorts.

## Gym class

Do:
• exercises
• running
• dancing or aerobics

# MAKING BOOKS

## stapled book

Take care when you staple!

stapler

## accordion book

## scrapbook

Stick in pictures you like from magazines.

## rough book

Tie paper together with string or yarn.

Or tie through each hole.

## workbooks

Recycle old workbooks. Write the lesson in each book.

Sums

writing

## bookmarks

First draw the shape. Then cut it out from thin cardboard.

Color it in.

# MAKING FOLDERS

Keep all your pieces of work safe in a folder. Make it out of thin cardboard. There are lots of different kinds to choose from.

### simple folder

Decorate.

### folder with 1 pocket

Tape folds down the end.

### folder with 2 pockets

side pockets          pockets at the bottom

## Make an art folder

You will need:

- large piece of cardboard
- fabric, glue, and adhesive tape
- craft knife and scissors
- ruler and pencil

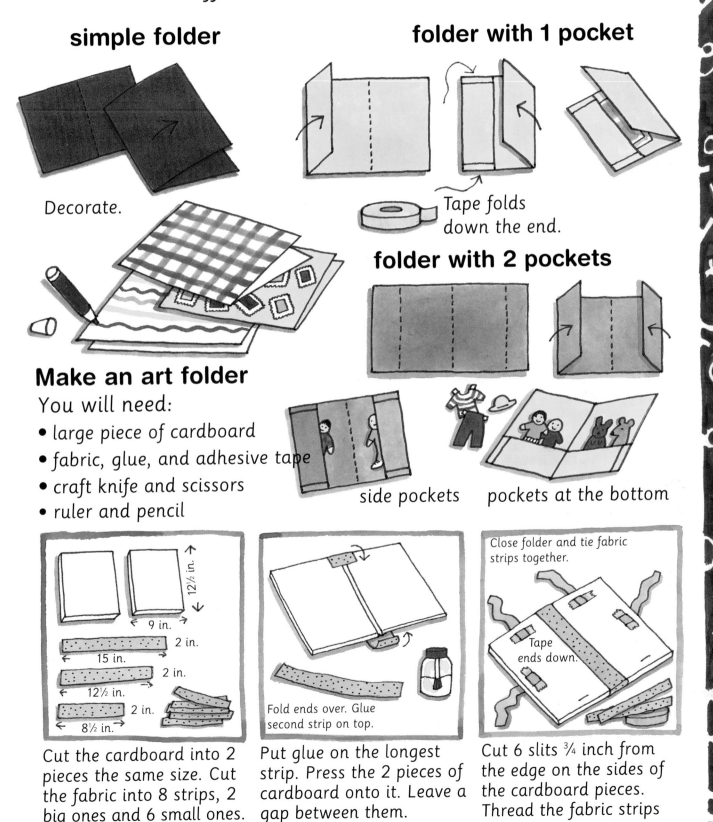

12½ in.

9 in.

2 in.
15 in.

2 in.
12½ in.

2 in.
8½ in.

Fold ends over. Glue second strip on top.

Close folder and tie fabric strips together.

Tape ends down.

Cut the cardboard into 2 pieces the same size. Cut the fabric into 8 strips, 2 big ones and 6 small ones.

Put glue on the longest strip. Press the 2 pieces of cardboard onto it. Leave a gap between them.

Cut 6 slits ¾ inch from the edge on the sides of the cardboard pieces. Thread the fabric strips through.

# GOOD WORK!

The teacher can grade the work when it is finished.
The teacher can also give homework.
This can be graded later.

red pen for grading

gold stars for very good work

## tests

Have short tests at the end of a lesson. Grade them.

## certificates

Make these to hand out to students.

Fill in the student's name and subject.

## trophies and awards

plastic yogurt container

Cut cardboard or plastic shapes.

Glue on aluminum foil.

Cover with aluminum foil.

Award these for good music and art.

## homework

Give reading, arithmetic, and writing to take home. It must be checked the next day!

# LET'S PLAY STORE

# CHARACTERS AND COSTUMES

Every store has storekeepers (owners or managers) and assistants to serve the customers. Stores also receive deliveries from the factories with more goods to sell.

**storekeepers**

Wear a uniform for some stores.

suit and tie to impress the customers

**customers**

**delivery person**

baseball or other cap

**paper hat for bakery**

Pull around and tape together.

Draw a sign or name on the front.

**apron**

**shopping bags**

sneakers

**purse, checkbook, credit cards, and money**

(see page 11)

# SETTING UP SHOP

Everything for sale must be easy to see and reach.
Arrange it on a table, or cloth on the ground.
Hang some things up.

**table**
with cloth

**chair**
for storekeeper

**boxes**

Put on table, for shelves.

**store signs**

closed open

open and closed, on one sign

SALE

Suzie's Sweet Sl

**box for small things**
all at one low price

Bargain Box all $1.

**scales**

**price labels**
Label all your goods before you open your store.

**plastic and paper bags**

# SWEET SHOP

Make pretend sweets from paper and playdough (see page 8). Don't be tempted to taste them though!
Sell real sweets or make your own.
Have fun wrapping them up.

## Make candies called fondant creams

1 cup powdered sugar makes approximately 20 creams.

You will need:

- powdered sugar
- lemon juice, orange juice, or peppermint extract
- food coloring (optional)
- sieve
- bowl
- wooden spoon
- rolling pin
- small, shaped cookie cutters

Sift sugar into bowl. Add very little juice or extract. Mix to stiff paste.

Dust board with powdered sugar.

Add 1 or 2 drops of coloring if desired. Mix well and roll out.

Use small, different-shaped cutters to make sweets.

## wrapping sweets

paper cases

plastic wrap

foil

## boxes

doilies

tongs

## gift wrapping

Add extras such as real or artificial flowers.

Recycle patterned gift wrap.

## bags

To curl paper or ribbons, pull along closed scissors.

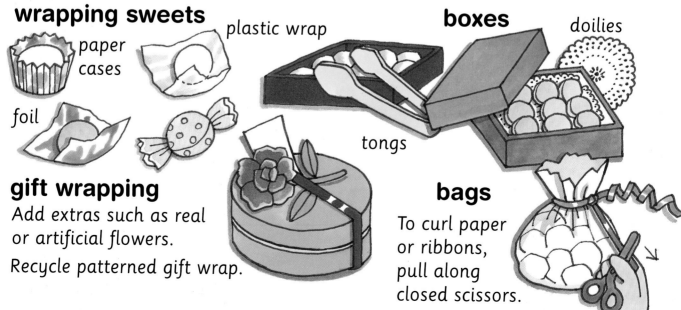

# CLOTHING STORE

This store is most fun when you have as many kinds of clothes as possible. Don't forget hats, shoes, socks, jewelry, and bags!

**mirrors**

**tape measure**

**hangers**

**clothes**
Make a line to hang clothes on.

**jewelry**
Display it in baskets or hang on a board.

**shoes**
Collect old shoe boxes for shoes.

sandals

choosing clothes for a special occasion

**belts**

# FRUIT AND VEGETABLE MARKET

Make your own fruit and vegetables with paper and paints. Follow these simple instructions.

1 Crinkle newspaper into fruit and vegetable shapes.

2 Wrap adhesive tape around the shapes.

4 Paint them white. Let them dry and then paint on different colors.

3 Tear some paper into small pieces. Glue them on the shapes.

5 Paint on details at the end.

prices

scales

baskets

Stick on paper leaves.

Make your favorite things.

bag with the top rolled down

34

# BAKERY

Make real bread, rolls, cakes, and biscuits, or make pretend versions. Include ready-made sandwiches.

**cardboard ring doughnuts**

**danishes**

Serve with tongs.

Use red pencil for danish fillings.

Stick cardboard ring on top.

cardboard biscuits

trays

**sandwiches**

## Make cheese biscuits

You will need:
- $3^1/_2$ oz. plain flour
- $^1/_4$ teaspoon salt
- sieve, bowl, and knife
- $2^1/_3$ oz. butter
- 3 tablespoons grated cheese
- 2–3 teaspoons water
- rolling pin
- cookie cutters (optional)

cardboard squares

filling painted or cut out of paper

Stuff socks with paper for bread.

5   10   BUNS

price and name flags

Cook until golden.

Sift the flour and salt into the bowl. Cut the butter into the flour and rub in with your fingertips.

Add the cheese. Mix to a stiff paste with the water. Roll out on a floured surface.

Cut into shapes. Place on a baking tray. Cook in a hot oven (400°F) for 15–20 minutes.

35

# BEAUTY PARLOR

This is the place to go to get made up for a special occasion such as a fancy party.

**clean paper towels**

To tie around customers' necks.

Give waiting customers comics to read and a drink.

Ask for adult help. Only use safe products and take great care around eyes! Follow instructions on products carefully.

**lips**
lipstick

**powder**

**face paints**

**tissues**

**face painting**

Make a chart of simple designs to show your customers. They can choose the one they like!

**mirror**

**cotton balls or pads**

# HAIRDRESSER'S

Make a hairdressing salon with chairs, a table, and mirror. Paint some big pictures of hairstyles to hang up.

**mirror**

**book of hairstyles**
See page 26 to make a book.

Name the styles.

spikey

Hairstyles

**pictures**

**comb**
Dipped in
water to
wet hair.

**mirror**
To show back
and sides.

**hair decorations**

**brush and comb**

**hair gel and color spray**

37

# GROCERY STORE

Keep all the empty packages from food you have at home. If you have lots and lots of friends to play with make your store a supermarket!

**basket**

Tape on a cardboard handle.

Make from a cardboard box.

**cartons**

**list**

beans
eggs
soap
milk
ice cream

**yogurt and cream**

Wash out old containers and re-cover tops with foil.

**cash register and play money**

**cold cuts and cheese**

Draw on paper, cut out, and stick onto cardboard. Cover with plastic wrap.

**grocery bags**

**rolls or biscuits**

Decorate cardboard tubes.

**fruit and vegetables**

Make with newspaper (see page 34), use plastic ones, or ask if you can borrow some real ones.

# LET'S PLAY THEATER

# PLANNING YOUR PLAY

Decide what play you want to put on. You can make it all up or use a well-known story. Divide it up into scenes with a rest for an intermission. Write down everyone's lines and rehearse.

## ☆ CINDERELLA ☆

This is one play you could do. But you can choose any story and follow the same advice for creating characters, costumes, props, and staging the show. Start with the script.

### SCENE 1

Kitchen at Cinderella's house.
Cinderella, Buttons (her only friend), and the Ugly sisters. Cinderella is cleaning when her sisters rush in.

We've been invited to a ball at the Palace!

Get on with your work, Cinderella!

I wish I could go but I have nothing to wear.

Never mind, Cinderella. I'm your friend.

The sisters leave to choose clothes for the ball. Suddenly the Fairy Godmother appears.

You SHALL go to the ball.

But you must leave at 12 o'clock.

Cinderella brings her a pumpkin and mice.

The Fairy Godmother waves her wand over them and gives her a carriage and a lovely dress.

Thank you Fairy Godmother. Goodbye!

## INTERMISSION

40

# SCENE 2

Ballroom at Palace.
Music. Cinderella and Prince dancing. Ugly sisters watching.
Clock strikes 12. Cinderella must go home.
Cinderella leaves but drops one of her shoes.

Oh no!
12 o'clock...
I must go.

I will marry whoever this shoe fits.

# SCENE 3

Kitchen at Cinderella's house.
Cinderella, Buttons, the Ugly sisters, and the Prince.

All the girls must try on this shoe.

The Ugly sisters try on the shoe but it's too small. Cinderella tries it on and of course it fits.

Cinderella will you marry me?

# SCENE 4

And they lived happily ever after...

Hooray!
Bravo, Cinderella!

THE END

# CHARACTERS AND COSTUMES

A play has to have actors and actresses. Add extra parts if there are lots of you. Play more than one part if there are too few. Boys can play girls' parts and girls play boys'. (This was very common in the past.) You will also need stagehands and maybe musicians. Don't forget to invite an audience!

Use very old clothes.

sweat suit

Cut edges into tatters.

Wear bright colors and patterns.

**Cinderella**

**Buttons**

**Ugly sisters**

old jacket

long socks over pants

tinsel in hair and as necklace

curtain for cloak

nightgown or robe

**Prince**

**Fairy Godmother**

**ushers and stagehands**
Wear black and white.

## buttons for Buttons!

cardboard circles

Cover with foil.

Glue or tape on clothes.

## Cinderella's rags

Cut patches from paper or material.

Stick on, or sew on with yarn.

## Ugly sisters

Wear lots of jewelry.

sparkly scarves for ball

slippers or high heels

## Cinderella's ball dress

Quick to put on. Use nightgown with net skirt on top.

## Fairy Godmother

For wand, stick silver or gold star onto stick.

## Make epaulettes for the Prince

You will need:
- cardboard and scissors
- thick yellow yarn or felt
- adhesive tape and glue
- yellow paint and brush

## glass slipper

Use your best shoe or a ballet slipper and put it on a cushion.

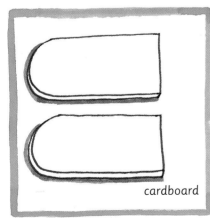

cardboard

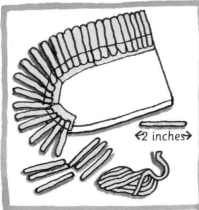

<2 inches>

Cut out 2 pieces of cardboard that will fit the shoulders.

Cut pieces of thick yellow yarn or felt. Tape them around one side of the cardboard.

Paint the top of the cardboard yellow. When dry, glue or tape onto the shoulders.

# MAKEUP AND HAIR

Use face paints and approved hair sprays that wash off easily. Ask adults to give you their old makeup.
Be careful of your eyes!

hair straggly

smudges
on face

**Cinderella in rags**

If hair is long, put it up with bow of net or ribbons. For short hair wear a hairband with a bow.

**Cinderella at the ball**

**Prince**

Use hair gel.

Comb down
or up.

glitter
spray for
hair

stars on
cheeks

**Fairy Godmother**

**Ugly sisters**

Use lots of makeup or face paints.

Draw on
eyelashes and
eyebrows.

colored
eye shadow

huge red lips

Tie hair into
bunches
with bows.

Use colored
gel or sprays.

beauty marks

# PAPERWORK

## posters

Advertise your play with posters.
Be sure to write all the important facts.

- Title
- Date
- Time
- Place
- Price of tickets

CINDERELLA

CINDERELLA

Write the title
on the outside.

## programs

Fold a piece of
paper in half.

Characters
Cinderella        Judy
                  Brown
Prince            David
                  Smith

Scene 1
Cinderella's kitchen

Inside, write:
- a list of characters with the names of their actors
- the scenes and where they take place.
Don't forget the intermission!

## tickets

Use different colored paper for adult and
child tickets. Sell them before the
performance. Collect them as people arrive.

## signs

Show scene signs and intermission signs to the audience.

adult
adult
adult
adult
adult

child
child
child
child
child

adult

child

scene
1

scene
2

intermission
10 minutes

# INTERMISSION

Have an intermission about halfway through your play or show, at the end of a scene. This is the time to serve refreshments to the audience.

## ushers

Ushers show people to their seats and collect tickets. They also sell programs. In the intermission they sell refreshments.

## refreshment tray

Cut down a cardboard box to form a shallow tray.
Tape a length of rope or tape across the bottom of the box and over the sides.

Tie the ends.

Make the tape long enough to go around the neck.

Balance the tray against the chest.

## flashlight

Ushers need a flashlight to show people to their seats in the dark.

## refreshments

### popcorn
Put into plastic cups.

### ice cream
Put into plastic cups with a teaspoon.

### cold drinks
Serve in plastic cups.

### other snacks
like chips or cookies

# MAKING PROPS

Here are some things to make for your play.
Remember to make everything large and bold so they
can be easily seen.

## invitations

Make 3 – for the 2 Ugly
sisters and Cinderella.

thick paper          Cut wavy edges.

## carriage

Cut out a window for
Cinderella to carry.

Add a
strong
handle.

## pumpkin and mice

Draw large pictures on
thin cardboard. Cut out.

## tiara and crowns

Make a tiara for the Fairy Godmother
and crowns for Cinderella and the
Prince when they marry at the end.

Measure the heads and cut out of paper.

## confetti

Cut up small pieces of
colored paper to throw at
the wedding.

Decorate with adhesive shapes.

# SCENERY

Hang old sheets or an old curtain across the back of the stage. Stick on cut-out paper pictures (then you can use them again). Make the pictures simple and bold.

**kitchen**

**ballroom**

**clock**

**lighting**

Darken the room and switch all the lights off at the end of each scene.

Draw large clock face on thin cardboard. Make the time 12 o'clock. Cut out.

Switch them on again in the intermission and play some music.

Play live music, if possible.

## music

Play tapes and CDs in the intermission, during the ball, and at the wedding.

Find something to ring or bang to signal 12 o'clock.